Pirate
with Molly on board

by Eddie McCartney and Alison Hedger

a fun musical in one setting for Primary Schools
using children of mixed ages and abilities

approximate duration 35 minutes

Suitable for class or year production, or whole small schools.
Five speaking parts, three of which have some solo singing;
groups of Pirates who dance a hornpipe and Islanders who sing together;
a chorus of singers

TEACHER'S BOOK
Complete with script and music

SONGS

1. My Name Is Blackbeard	Blackbeard + All
2. Diamonds Are The Gift For Me	Molly + All
3. Good Golly, Dear Molly	All
4. Smile (includes Pirates' Dance)	All
5. It's Wonderful To Have Some Friends	All + Pirate 1
6. Our Island Home	Islanders
7. This Cleaning Lark	All
FINALE Repeat 1. My Name Is Blackbeard	All

A matching tape cassette of the music for rehearsals and performances is available,
Order No. GA11060, with vocals included on side A and omitted on side B.

© Copyright 1998 Golden Apple Productions
A division of Chester Music Limited
8/9 Frith Street, London W1V 5TZ

Order No. GA11059

ISBN 0-7119-6825-X

Percy Prior's
£ 6.95

CAST LIST

* **Captain Blackbeard**	dressed as an outlawed sea captain
* **Pirate 1**	costume as expected
Pirate 2	
* **Molly, Blackbeard's wife**	in a full length dress
Chief Islander	with a headdress to denote his position

Non-speaking parts:

+ **Pirates**	dastardly buccaneers
Islanders	primitive native costume with bare feet
Chorus of Singers	sing lyrics marked All; also may provide sound effects and percussion if desired

* denotes solo singing and + denotes dancing
See page 24 for illustration of costumes

PROPS

mops and buckets
telescope
basket of exotic fruit
treasure casket overflowing with jewels
diamond necklace

ONE SET

The deck of a pirate sailing ship. A Jolly Roger flag, with a white skull and crossbones on a black background, is visible to audience.

MUSIC, SOUND EFFECTS AND DANCE

The matching tape cassette GA11060 has the music recorded on side A with vocals, but side B has the vocals omitted for rehearsing and performing to. The piano accompaniment is simple and chord symbols are given.

The children might like to make a recording of water splashing for use when the longboats are at sea. Try recording running taps, pouring jugs of water etc. Additional sound effects can be added as desired.

The music lends itself to hornpipe-like jigs or swinging around in pairs with linked crooked arms. Only the **Pirates' Dance** in Song 4 has been indicated in the script, so leaving further dancing as an option. Please repeat the music as necessary if you wish to include more dancing.

PIRATES! with Molly on board

Pirates on deck busily swabbing it with mops. Captain Blackbeard enters. Pirates stop working.

Blackbeard	No sign of any treasure ships yet?
Pirate 1	'Fraid not sir.
Pirate 2	They must have got wind that we're about, Captain.
Blackbeard	Could be. Fear of me makes them keep their distance. They all shake in their shoes when they hear my name!

SONG 1   MY NAME IS BLACKBEARD

Blackbeard   *1.*

My name is Blackbeard,
A pirate of some fame.
You must have heard of me,
I rule the Spanish Main.

All   *Refrain*

Blow you trade winds blow,
With a yo, ho, ho, ho, ho!
If a ship's about,
We'll search it out
And stow its treasure below, below.
And stow its treasure below!

Blackbeard   *2.*

My name is Blackbeard,
I tell you I don't boast.
I am the buccaneer
That sailors fear the most.

All   *Refrain*   **Blow you trade winds blow. . .**

Blackbeard   *3.*

My name is Blackbeard,
The captain of this crew.
No finer men have sailed
Upon the ocean blue.

All   *Refrain*

Blow you trade winds blow. . .
Yo, ho!

Pirates punch air above their heads with right arms and clenched fists on final Yo, ho!
Enter Molly, Blackbeard's wife.

Blackbeard	Hello dear wife.
Molly	As I am your "dear wife" I hope you haven't forgotten that today is my birthday.
Blackbeard	Er, no.

Molly		And my present?
Blackbeard		Well, yes!
Molly		You promised me diamonds.
Blackbeard		I know, but. . .
Molly		I don't want any "buts"!
Blackbeard		But Molly, I was hoping to get you the diamonds when we raided a treasure ship. We've been sailing for weeks and still no sign of any. Could be what the men are saying is true: "women on board bring bad luck".
Molly		Well, that's your problem. You promised me diamonds and that's what I'm going to have!

SONG 2   DIAMONDS ARE THE GIFT FOR ME

Molly   1.
**If you should be in any doubt,
I'm going to help you work it out.
Surely you must know,
For I have told you so.
Diamonds are the gift for me.**

All   *Refrain*
**Give me diamonds, diamonds.
Diamonds are the gift for me.**

Molly   2.
**You can't give me just anything.
I'm going to tell you what to bring.
Though I'm not adverse
To something for my purse,
Diamonds are the gift for me.**

All   *Refrain*   **Give me diamonds . . .**

At the end of the song the pirates lean on their mops.

Molly   You're supposed to be mopping. Get on with it! This ship is a disgrace.

The pirates start busily mopping. Molly flounces off. Blackbeard shrugs his shoulders.

Pirate 1   Captain, we are all absolutely fed up with this constant cleaning.

Captain   Don't blame me. It's your own fault. The last time we returned home Molly was so disgusted by the state of our ship that she decided to come along this time, just to show you how to keep a ship spick-and-span!

Blackbeard goes off.

Pirate 1
(to Pirate 2)   You could have offered Molly your parrot as a present.

Pirate 2	She wouldn't have taken it.
Pirate 1	Why not?
Pirate 2	'Cause it talks back!
Pirate 1	You know it's no laughing matter. Brushing, dusting and scrubbing is no work for pirates.

SONG 3   GOOD GOLLY, DEAR MOLLY

All   *Refrain*   **Good golly, dear Molly.**
Life is not so jolly
Since you came aboard.
Good golly, dear Molly.
It is such a folly.
We think perhaps you should have stayed at home.

spoken   **(Stayed at home.)**

1. **Don't you know that pirate men**
All like to stay in bed till ten?
We'll have you know that we object
To getting up to swab the deck.
Get up to swab the deck!

Refrain   **Good golly, dear Molly . . .**

2. **We don't know why all the fuss,**
Why this concern about some dust?
The outcome it is sure to be
That we will start a mutiny.
We'll start a mutiny!

Refrain   **Good golly, dear Molly . . .**

Blackbeard returns.

Blackbeard	I don't know what I'm going to do. Molly insists on having diamonds. Where am I going to get them from today?
Pirate 1	Nothing but problems.
Pirate 2	Too true. Nothing but problems – the Captain has to get Molly her diamonds and we have to do all Molly's cleaning.
Blackbeard	Cheer up lads. Life's not that bad. No use grousing. Just think of the many sticky situations we've been in before and always pulled through and come out smiling.
Pirate 1	You're right Captain. Look on the bright side I say. Who knows, a treasure ship might be just over the horizon.
Blackbeard	That's true. Then I can give Molly her darned diamonds and we can set sail for home.

SONG 4   SMILE (includes Pirates' Dance)

All

Life is what you make of it.
How do we face up to it
When everything goes wrong, wrong, wrong?
Don't accept that it is fate.
Make a change, it's not too late.
Just smile and carry on.

Refrain

Even though you might be down,
Things will get better. Please don't frown!
Though life's dim you still can grin.
Though you might be down in luck,
Soon you'll be on the up and up.
Life is what you make of it.
Smile, smile, smile.
Life is what you make of it. Smile!

twice

*All the
Pirates dance
during the
repeat*

Pirate 1	I suppose one day you'll settle down ashore, Captain?
Blackbeard	I suppose so. Molly wants me to. She gets lonely at home alone.
Pirate 1	It's a hard life being a pirate's wife.
Pirate 2	And an even harder job being a pirate!

Pirate 1 looks across the sea with his telescope.

Pirate 1	Land ahoy Sir! We're fast approaching an island.

Blackbeard takes the telescope and looks for himself.

Blackbeard	Some of the islanders have taken to a boat and are rowing out to meet us. Lower the sails. Cast the anchor. We'll make them welcome. They look friendly to me. Men, tie up their boat and help them aboard.

Pirates busily carry out Blackbeard's instructions. The chief of the islanders clambers on stage along with a group of islanders. They present Blackbeard with a basket of exotic fruits.

Blackbeard	Thank you very much. Very kind I'm sure.
Chief	Welcome to our island. We don't have many visitors. Well, not friendly ones, that is.
Blackbeard	What do you mean?

The Chief looks out to sea and is suddenly very agitated.

Chief	Oh no! Help, help.
Blackbeard	What's the matter?
Chief	See that boat approaching our island? (*All nod yes*) It's a raiding party from a neighbouring island. They steal from us. We are peace-loving island people, but they are not. They make our lives miserable.
Blackbeard	Is that so? Well, they've met their match in us!

Blackbeard turns to Pirates 1 and 2

Blackbeard	You two, stay here with the ship. The rest of you come with me. Lower the longboat. Row like mad. We'll soon put a stop to this merry game!

Blackbeard, rest of pirates, the Chief and his islanders exit. Pirates 1 and 2 watch excitedly from the ship.

Pirate 1	Look! Blackbeard has one of the raiders in an arm lock.
Pirate 2	Wow! We're giving those raiders a run for their money! What a right thrashing they're getting!
Pirate 1	Crumbs! The raiders have scarpered. They're off – we've won!
Pirates 1 and 2	Hooray! (*They throw arms up in a victory wave*)
Pirate 2	That lot won't be back in a hurry. No need for the islanders to worry any more about that load of wimps.

Blackbeard clambers back on board along with pirates, the Chief and his islanders. The Chief is carrying a treasure casket.

Blackbeard (*Calling*)	Molly. Molly! Come here! (*she enters*) The island Chief has a present for me to show his thanks for chasing that rabble off for once and for all.

The Chief opens the casket.

Chief	We found these jewels hidden in a cave many years ago. Please help yourself, Captain. They are of no real value to us. (*He offers the casket to Blackbeard, who guides Molly to see the jewels*)
Blackbeard	There you are my dear. Take your pick from this lot!

Molly selects a diamond necklace and puts it on.

Molly	Thank you so very much. Just what I wanted for my birthday.
Chief	We will always be grateful to your husband for what he did today. Please remember us when you wear the necklace.
Molly	Thank you, I will. You will always be our special friends.

SONG 5   IT'S WONDERFUL TO HAVE SOME FRIENDS

All		1.	**It's just great to know we're not alone. We have some friends who are our very own.**
	Refrain		**It's wonderful, wonderful, It's wonderful to have some friends.**
Pirate 1 (*to Pirate 2*)		2.	**I know that I can on you depend. You'll always have a helping hand to lend.**
All	*Refrain*		**It's wonderful, wonderful, It's wonderful to have some friends.**
All		3.	**Though we might be many miles apart. There'll be a place for you within our hearts.**
	Refrain		**It's wonderful, wonderful, It's wonderful to have some friends.**

Chief	Captain, why don't you, your wife and all your men come and live on our island?
Blackbeard	Well, that's a mighty fine offer, but we'd need to think about it long and hard. It would mean a very different life for us.
Chief	Our island is a wonderful place. I'm sure you'd be very happy.

SONG 6   OUR ISLAND HOME

Islanders

1. **Soft sea breezes they caress us,
Strolling on the shore.
Peacefulness is all around us.
Could we ask for more?**

Refrain
**Don't you feel it in the air?
Happiness is everywhere.
Stay with us and never roam
From our island home.
Our island home.**

2. **Sunny days are always with us,
Cloudless are the skies.
We have everything provided
In this paradise.**

Refrain
Don't you feel it in the air? . . .

3. **Should you stay upon our island,
Passing time will tell,
If you'll always be enchanted
By its magic spell.**

Refrain
Don't you feel it in the air? . . .

Blackbeard	Thank you all for your kind invitation. It is certainly very tempting but I don't think the life would suit any of us in the long run. I think I speak for all the men when I say we're better off with life as we know it.
Chief	Well then, we must say goodbye, and thank you for everything.
Blackbeard	Not at all.

Exit Chief and islanders.

Blackbeard	Weigh the anchor. Full sail. We're homeward bound.
Pirates 1 and 2	Aye, aye, Sir!
Molly	(*Taking Blackbeard's arm*) I'll be glad to get home. The truth is, I don't much like the life on board ship.
Blackbeard	Yes, it will be good to see home waters once more.
Molly	But will you manage to keep the ship clean and tidy when I'm not with you? For I'm not planning on coming again.

Blackbeard	We most certainly will, won't we men?
(All nod vigorously)	
Molly	But will you miss me?
Blackbeard	Of course we'll miss you my dear. We'll be thinking of you every day! . . . whilst we're cleaning!!

SONG 7   THIS CLEANING LARK

All

1. Molly dear this cleaning lark,
    We find it so exciting!
    If a treasure ship comes near
    We'll have no time for fighting.

    Refrain
    Brush and dust and scrub.
    We will brush and dust and scrub.
    Wash the decks till backs they crack.
    We'll never slack and that's a fact.
    Brush and dust and scrub.

2. Molly dear away at sea,
    We will for you be pining!
    But we will return to you,
    The ship all clean and shining.

    Refrain
    Brush and dust and scrub . . .

Blackbeard   Homeward bound! And with a bit of good luck we'll meet a treasure ship on the way.

FINALE   Repeat Song 1   MY NAME IS BLACKBEARD
(*see page 3*)

Everyone sings the song this time, with slightly altered words. (The Refrain remains unchanged)

1. *His* name is Blackbeard,
    A pirate of some fame.
    You must of heard of *him*,
    He rules the Spanish Main.

2. *His* name is Blackbeard,
    We tell you *we* don't boast.
    He is the buccaneer
    That sailors fear the most.

3. *His* name is Blackbeard,
    The captain of this crew.
    No finer men have sailed
    Upon the ocean blue.

1
MY NAME IS BLACKBEARD (ALSO FINALE—*ALL*)

Blackbeard + All
Cue: They all shake in their shoes when they hear my name!
Finale cue: And with a bit of good luck we'll meet a treasure ship on the way.

For FINALE: everyone sings the song this time. Slightly alter words in verses 1, 2 and 3.

1. **His** name is Blackbeard,
    A pirate of some fame.
    You must of heard of him,
    He rules the Spanish Main.

2. **His** name is Blackbeard,
    We tell you we don't boast.
    He is the buccaneer
    That sailors fear the most.

3. **His** name is Blackbeard,
    The captain of this crew.
    No finer men have sailed
    Upon the ocean blue.

11

DIAMONDS ARE THE GIFT FOR ME

Molly + All
Cue: You promised me diamonds and that's what I'm going to have!

Molly:
1. If you should be in an - y doubt, _____ I'm going to help you work it out. _____
2. You can't give me just an - y - thing. _____ I'm going to tell you what to bring. _____

Surely you must know, for I have told you
Though I'm not adverse to something for my

so. Diamonds are the gift for me.
purse, diamonds are the gift for me.

Refrain

All: Give me diamonds, diamonds.

(well marked bass)

Diamonds are the gift for me.

13

3
GOOD GOLLY, DEAR MOLLY

All
Cue: Brushing, dusting and scrubbing is no work for pirates.

SMILE (includes Pirates' Dance)

All
Cue: Then I can give Molly her darned diamonds and we can set sail for home.

Full of optimism and energy ♩. = 108

Life is what you make of it. How do we face up to it
Don't ac-cept that it is fate. Make a change, it's not too late.

when ev - ery - thing goes wrong, wrong, wrong?
Just smile and car - ry

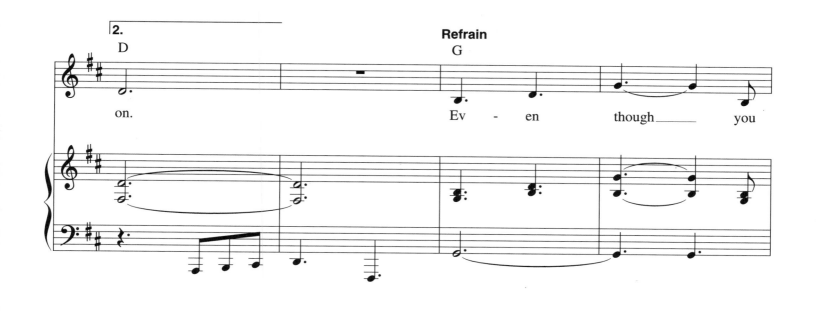

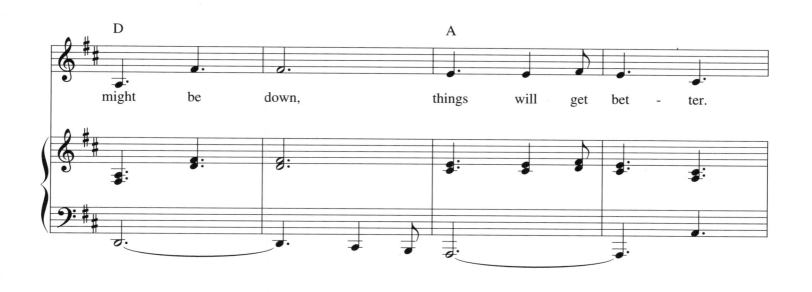

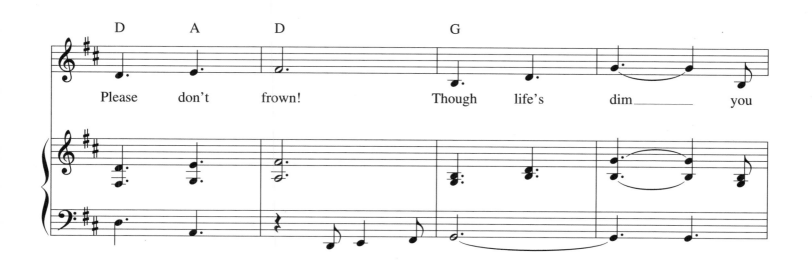

17

5
IT'S WONDERFUL TO HAVE SOME FRIENDS

All + Pirate 1
Cue: You will always be our special friends.

6
OUR ISLAND HOME

Islanders
Cue: I'm sure you'd be very happy.

With a South Seas Island feel! Dreamily ♩ = 108

1. Soft sea breez - es
2. Sun - ny days are
3. Should you stay up -

they car - ess us, strol - ling on the shore.
al - ways with us, cloud - less are the skies.
- on our is - land, pass - ing time will tell,

continue with pedal

Peace - ful - ness is all a - round us. Could we ask for more?
We have ev - ery - thing pro - vid - ed in this par - a - dise.
if you'll al - ways be en - chant - ed by its mag - ic spell.

Refrain

Don't you feel it in the air? Hap - pi - ness is

ev - ery - where. Stay with us and nev - er roam from our

is - land home. Our is - land home.

7
THIS CLEANING LARK

All
Cue: We'll be thinking of you every day! . . . whilst we're cleaning!!

With false sincerity! Lots of energy ♩. = 100

1. Mol - ly dear this clean - ing lark, we find it so ex - cit - ing! If a trea - sure ship comes near we'll
2. Mol - ly dear a - way at sea, we will for you be pin - ing! But we will re - turn to you, the

FINALE: Repeat song 1 see pages 10–11